I'm Kind Of Awesome

KNOCK KNOCK®

LOS ANGELES, CALIFORNIA

Created, published, and distributed by Knock Knock
11111 Jefferson Blvd. #5167
Culver City, CA 90231
knockknockstuff.com
Knock Knock is a registered trademark of Knock Knock LLC
Inner-Truth is a registered trademark of Knock Knock LLC

UPC: 825703-61211-0

10 9 8 7 6 5 4 3 2 1

WORD ON THE STREET IS THAT YOU'RE KIND OF AWESOME.

Yeah you are! True story. But maybe you're doubting? Oh, the doubting. Or maybe you don't doubt your awesomeness (congratulations), but being an awesome person, you know you can't walk down the street proclaiming it unless you want people to give you a whole lot of space. Whether you're working your way toward awesome and want to record the progress, trying to reclaim your awesomeness after a setback, or looking for a place to revel in awesomeness, this journal is sure to come in handy.

A journal is your safe space to work out your thoughts and ideas in your journey toward awesomeness. It's also where you can celebrate your fantastic feats without anyone throwing shade your way.

The word "awesome" gets tossed around a lot. It's a good idea to re-mind yourself what it means, so you can decide what kind of awesome you want to be. Here is the definition according to Merriam-Webster:

Causing feelings of fear and wonder : causing feelings of awe : extremely good

> 1: expressive of awe
> 2a: inspiring awe
> 2b: terrific, extraordinary

Most of us are aiming for extremely good, terrific, and/or super extraordinary. But no one is saying you can't aim to truly inspire awe. You could even aspire to cause feelings of fear and wonder, particularly if you are an evil genius or the parent of small children.

Are you worried that declaring yourself awesome is not entirely healthy? Don't worry; a soupçon of narcissism isn't bad. Susan Krauss Whitbourne, in her *Psychology Today* article "The Healthy Side of Narcissism," argues that mild narcissism can actually be good for your well-being. Researchers have called this "adaptive narcissism," which helps people become self-sufficient, self-confident, better at coping with anxiety, and effective leaders. How do you know when you've gone too far? In *O, the Oprah Magazine*, life coach Martha Beck lays out how you can differentiate healthy self-esteem from narcissism. "Go to the person in your life who reeks of self-esteem and ask, 'In what ways do you think you need to grow or change?' If the person is psychologically healthy, the list will be as long as your leg. That's because real self-esteem is based on finding areas where we can improve ourselves and honestly working to overcome problems. Healthy people know that they are always a work in progress. Narcissists, on the other hand, will tell you they have nothing to change."

Take a page from Ms. Beck and recognize that self-esteem takes work. Use this journal to log that process and nurture healthy awesomeness.

Specialists agree that in order to reap the benefits of journaling you have to stick with it, quasi-daily, for as little as five minutes at a time (at least fifteen minutes, however, is best), even on the days when awesomeness seems a distant memory. Finding regular writing times and comfortable locations can help with consistency. If you find yourself unable to muster a single awesome sentiment, do not stress. Instead, use the quotes inside this journal as a jumping-off point for observations and explorations.

What should you write about? The journal is your oyster. Keep track of the ways you want to grow and change. Keep a list of awesome people whom you want to emulate, and write about what makes them so spectacular. Hold forth on the things you like about yourself. List daily successes, whether success is writing a great report or just taking a shower that day. When you do something awkward or stupid, write about that as well. Recognizing and accepting your foibles makes you even more awesome.

Write whatever comes, and don't criticize it; journaling is a means of self-reflection, not a structured composition. In other words, spew. Finally, determine a home for your journal where you can reference it when you're feeling awesome or for that matter, not so awesome.

The great twenty-first century thinker and awesomeness role model Barney Stinson truly knew how to express his greatness: "In my body, where the shame gland should be, there is a second awesome gland." You've got awesome inside of you, too. Embrace and nurture it. Lots of idiots think they're awesome, but you really kind of are. True story.

And all the colors
I am inside

Have not been
invented yet.

Shel Silverstein

Why I'm Kind Of Awesome Today:

MY AWESOMENESS GRADE FOR TODAY:

☐ A-   ☐ A   ☐ A+   ☐ A++

I'm the most important person in the lives of almost everyone I know and a good number of the people I've never even met.

David Sedaris

Why I'm Kind Of Awesome Today:

MY AWESOMENESS GRADE FOR TODAY:

☐ A-   ☐ A   ☐ A+   ☐ A++

I always said I was like those round-bottomed circus dolls—you know, those dolls you could push down and they'd come back up? I've always been like that. I've always said, "No matter what happens, if I get pushed down, I'm going to come right back up."

Doris Day

Why I'm Kind Of Awesome Today:

MY AWESOMENESS GRADE FOR TODAY:

□ A-   □ A   □ A+   □ A++

I'd always vaguely expected to outgrow my limitations.

Gretchen Rubin

Why I'm Kind Of Awesome Today:

....

....

....

....

....

....

....

....

....

....

....

....

MY AWESOMENESS GRADE FOR TODAY:

☐ **A-**   ☐ **A**   ☐ **A+**   ☐ **A++**

The first time I didn't feel it, but this time I feel it, and I can't deny the fact that you like me, right now, you like me!

Sally Field

Why I'm Kind Of Awesome Today:

....

....

....

....

....

....

....

....

....

....

....

....

....

MY AWESOMENESS GRADE FOR TODAY:

☐ **A-**   ☐ **A**   ☐ **A+**   ☐ **A++**

I can have oodles of charm when I want to.

Kurt Vonnegut

Why I'm Kind Of Awesome Today:

MY AWESOMENESS GRADE FOR TODAY:

☐ A-   ☐ A   ☐ A+   ☐ A++

Look at the sky: that is for you. Look at each person's face as you pass on the street: those faces are for you. And the street itself, and the ground under the street, and the ball of fire underneath the ground: all these things are for you.

Miranda July

Why I'm Kind Of Awesome Today:

Some of us can't help it if we're ravishing.

Harvey Fierstein

Why I'm Kind Of Awesome Today:

MY AWESOMENESS GRADE FOR TODAY:

☐ A-   ☐ A   ☐ A+   ☐ A++

I think I may be the voice of my generation. Or at least a voice of a generation.

Lena Dunham

Why I'm Kind Of Awesome Today:

No need to hurry. No need to sparkle. No need to be anybody but oneself.

Virginia Woolf

Why I'm Kind Of Awesome Today:

....

....

....

....

....

....

....

....

....

....

....

....

MY AWESOMENESS GRADE FOR TODAY:

☐ A-   ☐ A   ☐ A+   ☐ A++

It was possible to feel superior to other people and like a misfit at the same time.

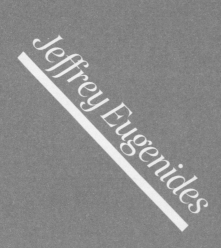

Jeffrey Eugenides

Why I'm Kind Of Awesome Today:

MY AWESOMENESS GRADE FOR TODAY:

☐ **A-**   ☐ **A**   ☐ **A+**   ☐ **A++**

You also have to know what sparks the light in you so that you, in your own way, can illuminate the world.

Oprah Winfrey

Why I'm Kind Of Awesome Today:

I want the title. Not just the money. The title. I'm a champion. I already have money.

Roberto Duran

Why I'm Kind Of Awesome Today:

MY AWESOMENESS GRADE FOR TODAY:

☐ **A-**   ☐ **A**   ☐ **A+**   ☐ **A++**

I'd rather be myself...
Myself and nasty.
Not somebody else,
however jolly.

Aldous Huxley

Why I'm Kind Of Awesome Today:

....

....

....

....

....

....

....

....

....

....

....

....

....

MY AWESOMENESS GRADE FOR TODAY:

☐ A- ☐ A ☐ A+ ☐ A++

I am so smart.
I am so smart.
I am so smart.
I am so smart.
S-M-R-T—
I mean S-M-A-R-T.

Homer Simpson

Why I'm Kind Of Awesome Today:

MY AWESOMENESS GRADE FOR TODAY:

□ A-   □ A   □ A+   □ A++

I personally like being unique. I like being my own person with my own style and my own opinions and my own toothbrush.

Ellen DeGeneres

Why I'm Kind Of Awesome Today:

....

....

....

....

....

....

....

....

....

....

....

....

MY AWESOMENESS GRADE FOR TODAY:

☐ A-   ☐ A   ☐ A+   ☐ A++

Future hipsters will love me ironically.

Mindy Kaling

Why I'm Kind Of Awesome Today:

MY AWESOMENESS GRADE FOR TODAY:

☐ A-   ☐ A   ☐ A+   ☐ A++

My life changed when I focused on what I was, what I was good at, what I liked most about myself and what made me stand out ... then I didn't have to worry about being the funniest or the most popular or the prettiest. I was the best me and I only ever tried to be that.

Issa Rae

Why I'm Kind Of Awesome Today:

....

....

....

....

....

....

....

....

....

....

....

....

....

MY AWESOMENESS GRADE FOR TODAY:

☐ **A-**   ☐ **A**   ☐ **A+**   ☐ **A++**

Don't worry where I am. I'll tell you when I get there.

Lawrence Taylor

Why I'm Kind Of Awesome Today:

MY AWESOMENESS GRADE FOR TODAY:

☐ A-   ☐ A   ☐ A+   ☐ A++

If I abstain from fun
and such,

I'll probably amount
to much;

But I shall stay the
way I am,

Because I do not
give a damn.

Dorothy Parker

Why I'm Kind Of Awesome Today:

MY AWESOMENESS GRADE FOR TODAY:

☐ A-   ☐ A   ☐ A+   ☐ A++

Like a fish which swims calmly in deep water, I felt all about me the secure supporting pressure of my own life. Ragged, inglorious, and apparently purposeless, but my own.

Iris Murdoch

Why I'm Kind Of Awesome Today:

....

....

....

....

....

....

....

....

....

....

....

....

MY AWESOMENESS GRADE FOR TODAY:

☐ A-   ☐ A   ☐ A+   ☐ A++

You haven't lived until you've basked in the adoration of the people.

Jerry Spinelli

Why I'm Kind Of Awesome Today:

MY AWESOMENESS GRADE FOR TODAY:

☐ A-   ☐ A   ☐ A+   ☐ A++

I feel pretty

Oh, so pretty

That the city should give me its key

A committee should be organized to honor me.

Stephen Sondheim

Why I'm Kind Of Awesome Today:

The issue is to accept who you are and revel in that.

Mitch Albom

Why I'm Kind Of Awesome Today:

MY AWESOMENESS GRADE FOR TODAY:

□ A-   □ A   □ A+   □ A++

When I was a child, my mother said to me, "If you become a soldier you'll be a general. If you become a monk you'll end up as the Pope." Instead, I became a painter and wound up as Picasso.

Pablo Picasso

Why I'm Kind Of Awesome Today:

Confidence has nothing to do with ability.

Augusten Burroughs

Why I'm Kind Of Awesome Today:

MY AWESOMENESS GRADE FOR TODAY:

□ A-   □ A   □ A+   □ A++

Alone had always felt like an actual place to me, as if it weren't a state of being, but rather a room where I could retreat to be who I really was.

Cheryl Strayed

Why I'm Kind Of Awesome Today:

MY AWESOMENESS GRADE FOR TODAY:

□ A-   □ A   □ A+   □ A++

You your best thing.

Toni Morrison

Why I'm Kind Of Awesome Today:

....

....

....

....

....

....

....

....

....

....

....

MY AWESOMENESS GRADE FOR TODAY:

☐ A-   ☐ A   ☐ A+   ☐ A++

What I came to realize is that fear, that's the worst of it. That's the real enemy. So, get up, get out in the real world and you kick that bastard as hard you can right in the teeth.

Walter White (Breaking Bad)

Why I'm Kind Of Awesome Today:

MY AWESOMENESS GRADE FOR TODAY:

☐ A-   ☐ A   ☐ A+   ☐ A++

I've always been a hugger ... If we all hugged more, the world would be a better place.

Taylor Swift

Why I'm Kind Of Awesome Today:

....

....

....

....

....

....

....

....

....

....

....

....

MY AWESOMENESS GRADE FOR TODAY:

☐ A-   ☐ A   ☐ A+   ☐ A++

I was someone with not much self-belief at all and yet in this one thing in my life I believed. That was the one thing in my life. I felt "I can tell a story."

J.K. Rowling

Why I'm Kind Of Awesome Today:

MY AWESOMENESS GRADE FOR TODAY:

☐ A-   ☐ A   ☐ A+   ☐ A++

Insult my sexual prowess, my intellect, but not my pancakes.

Moby

Why I'm Kind Of Awesome Today:

MY AWESOMENESS GRADE FOR TODAY:

□ A-   □ A   □ A+   □ A++

I'm young and strong, there isn't anything I can't do.

Ann Petry

Why I'm Kind Of Awesome Today:

MY AWESOMENESS GRADE FOR TODAY:

☐ A-   ☐ A   ☐ A+   ☐ A++

Off the pillow and into the air

I'm ready 'cause it's my day

Situation: it's all possible

Everything is going my way.

Why I'm Kind Of Awesome Today:

MY AWESOMENESS GRADE FOR TODAY:

☐ A-   ☐ A   ☐ A+   ☐ A++

Your true being is connected to all that exists.

Deepak Chopra

Why I'm Kind Of Awesome Today:

MY AWESOMENESS GRADE FOR TODAY:

□ A-   □ A   □ A+   □ A++

Once I had asked God for one or two extra inches in height, but instead he made me as tall as the sky, so high that I could not measure myself.

Malala Yousafzai

Why I'm Kind Of Awesome Today:

MY AWESOMENESS GRADE FOR TODAY:

☐ A-   ☐ A   ☐ A+   ☐ A++

There's not a thing wrong with you, you're right all the way through.

Emma Donoghue

Why I'm Kind Of Awesome Today:

MY AWESOMENESS GRADE FOR TODAY:

□ **A-**   □ **A**   □ **A+**   □ **A++**

I don't want anybody telling me what I'm supposed to look like. Or tell me that I'm wrong because I look a certain way. Or not the way they think I should be looking.

Whoopi Goldberg

Why I'm Kind Of Awesome Today:

MY AWESOMENESS GRADE FOR TODAY:

☐ A-   ☐ A   ☐ A+   ☐ A++

I'm a mix of vain and humble, flawed and flawless.

Gabourey Sidibe

Why I'm Kind Of Awesome Today:

MY AWESOMENESS GRADE FOR TODAY:

□ A-   □ A   □ A+   □ A++

I just decided to believe my own hype.

Amy Schumer

Why I'm Kind Of Awesome Today:

MY AWESOMENESS GRADE FOR TODAY:

□ A-   □ A   □ A+   □ A++

I'm me, and I like that there are people who have an appreciation for that.

Zooey Deschanel

Why I'm Kind Of Awesome Today:

I didn't ask to be born hot.

Ja'mie King

Why I'm Kind Of Awesome Today:

....

....

....

....

....

....

....

....

....

....

....

MY AWESOMENESS GRADE FOR TODAY:

☐ A-   ☐ A   ☐ A+   ☐ A++

I'm working on
my own life story.
I don't mean I'm
putting it together;
no, I'm taking
it apart.

Margaret Atwood

Why I'm Kind Of Awesome Today:

The man who does not value himself, cannot value anything or anyone.

Ayn Rand

Why I'm Kind Of Awesome Today:

MY AWESOMENESS GRADE FOR TODAY:

☐ **A-**   ☐ **A**   ☐ **A+**   ☐ **A++**

I am the only person in the world I should like to know thoroughly.

Oscar Wilde

——— Why I'm Kind Of Awesome Today: ———

MY AWESOMENESS GRADE FOR TODAY:

☐ A-   ☐ A   ☐ A+   ☐ A++

Helped are those who are content to be themselves; they will never lack mystery in their lives and the joys of self-discovery will be constant.

Alice Walker

Why I'm Kind Of Awesome Today:

MY AWESOMENESS GRADE FOR TODAY:

☐ A-　　　☐ A　　　☐ A+　　　☐ A++

All I know is that I'm going to do whatever makes me feel comfortable, and I'm gonna do whatever I want to do and hope that the essence of me and what people liked about me in the beginning will come through.

Tig Notaro

Why I'm Kind Of Awesome Today:

....

....

....

....

....

....

....

....

....

....

....

....

MY AWESOMENESS GRADE FOR TODAY:

☐ A-   ☐ A   ☐ A+   ☐ A++

I've done it all, and I've loved every trashy minute of it.

John Waters

Why I'm Kind Of Awesome Today:

MY AWESOMENESS GRADE FOR TODAY:

☐ **A-**   ☐ **A**   ☐ **A+**   ☐ **A++**

Every day, I define myself. I know who I am today. I don't promise you anything for tomorrow.

Salma Hayek

——— Why I'm Kind Of Awesome Today: ———

....

....

....

....

....

....

....

....

....

....

....

....

MY AWESOMENESS GRADE FOR TODAY:

□ A-   □ A   □ A+   □ A++

Does my sexiness
upset you?

Does it come as
a surprise

That I dance like I've
got diamonds

At the meeting of
my thighs?

Maya Angelou

— Why I'm Kind Of Awesome Today: —

MY AWESOMENESS GRADE FOR TODAY:

☐ A-   ☐ A   ☐ A+   ☐ A++

We do what we do, because of who we are. If we did otherwise, we would not be ourselves.

Neil Gaiman

Why I'm Kind Of Awesome Today:

MY AWESOMENESS GRADE FOR TODAY:

☐ A-   ☐ A   ☐ A+   ☐ A++

Dressing badly has been a refuge much of my life, a way of compelling others to engage with my mind, not my physical presence.

Sonia Sotomayor

Why I'm Kind Of Awesome Today:

....

....

....

....

....

....

....

....

....

....

....

....

MY AWESOMENESS GRADE FOR TODAY:

□ A-   □ A   □ A+   □ A++

I can be me. I can be whoever because I'm true to me.

Tupac Shakur

Why I'm Kind Of Awesome Today:

....

....

....

....

....

....

....

....

....

....

....

....

....

....

....

MY AWESOMENESS GRADE FOR TODAY:

☐ A-   ☐ A   ☐ A+   ☐ A++

Don't you ever let a person make you feel bad because you love something they decided is only for nerds. You're loving a thing that's for you.

Wil Wheaton

Why I'm Kind Of Awesome Today:

MY AWESOMENESS GRADE FOR TODAY:

☐ A-   ☐ A   ☐ A+   ☐ A++

I'm a fountain of blood

In the shape of a girl.

DATE:

Why I'm Kind Of Awesome Today:

MY AWESOMENESS GRADE FOR TODAY:

☐ A-   ☐ A   ☐ A+   ☐ A++

Follow your inner moonlight; don't hide the madness.

Allen Ginsberg

Why I'm Kind Of Awesome Today:

MY AWESOMENESS GRADE FOR TODAY:

☐ A-   ☐ A   ☐ A+   ☐ A++

When I am in my painting, I'm not aware of what I'm doing ... I have no fears about making changes, destroying the image, etc., because the painting has a life of its own.

Jackson Pollock

DATE:

— Why I'm Kind Of Awesome Today: —

MY AWESOMENESS GRADE FOR TODAY:

□ A-   □ A   □ A+   □ A++

You want me
down on Earth

But I am up
in space.

Icona Pop

Why I'm Kind Of Awesome Today:

MY AWESOMENESS GRADE FOR TODAY:

□ **A-**   □ **A**   □ **A+**   □ **A++**

A strong sense of identity gives man an idea he can do no wrong; too little accomplishes the same.

Djuna Barnes

Why I'm Kind Of Awesome Today:

MY AWESOMENESS GRADE FOR TODAY:

☐ A-   ☐ A   ☐ A+   ☐ A++

I am who I am, doing what I came to do.

Audre Lorde

Why I'm Kind Of Awesome Today:

....

....

....

....

....

....

....

....

....

....

....

....

MY AWESOMENESS GRADE FOR TODAY:

□ **A-**   □ **A**   □ **A+**   □ **A++**

Picture you talking to your own daughter, or your younger sister—because you would tell your younger sister or your daughter that she was beautiful, and you wouldn't be lying. Because she is. And so are you.

Amy Poehler

Why I'm Kind Of Awesome Today:

MY AWESOMENESS GRADE FOR TODAY:

☐ A-   ☐ A   ☐ A+   ☐ A++

I'm just an
advertisement

For a version
of myself.

David Byrne

Why I'm Kind Of Awesome Today:

MY AWESOMENESS GRADE FOR TODAY:

☐ A-   ☐ A   ☐ A+   ☐ A++

I got their attention,
I got their approval,
their admiration, their
approbation, and their
applause. And those are
the only A's I wanted, and
I got 'em.

George Carlin

Why I'm Kind Of Awesome Today:

MY AWESOMENESS GRADE FOR TODAY:

□ A-   □ A   □ A+   □ A++

The universe and the light of the stars come through me. I am the crescent moon put up over the gate to the festival.

Rumi

Why I'm Kind Of Awesome Today:

....

....

....

....

....

....

....

....

....

....

....

....

MY AWESOMENESS GRADE FOR TODAY:

☐ **A-**   ☐ **A**   ☐ **A+**   ☐ **A++**

I am a champion And you're gonna hear me roar.

Katy Perry

Why I'm Kind Of Awesome Today:

MY AWESOMENESS GRADE FOR TODAY:

☐ **A-**   ☐ **A**   ☐ **A+**   ☐ **A++**

I'm eighty years old and I'm twerking.

Joan Rivers

Why I'm Kind Of Awesome Today:

MY AWESOMENESS GRADE FOR TODAY:

☐ A- ☐ A ☐ A+ ☐ A++

I think I'll try defying gravity And you can't pull me down.

Stephen Schwartz

— Why I'm Kind Of Awesome Today: —

MY AWESOMENESS GRADE FOR TODAY:

□ A-   □ A   □ A+   □ A++

Don't call me crazy. I'm a survivor. I do what I have to do to survive.

Stieg Larsson

Why I'm Kind Of Awesome Today:

....

....

....

....

....

....

....

....

....

....

....

....

....

MY AWESOMENESS GRADE FOR TODAY:

☐ A-   ☐ A   ☐ A+   ☐ A++

I'm not going to censor myself to comfort your ignorance.

Jon Stewart

Why I'm Kind Of Awesome Today:

MY AWESOMENESS GRADE FOR TODAY:

□ A-   □ A   □ A+   □ A++

You need not apologize for being brilliant, talented, gorgeous, rich, or smart.

Marianne Williamson

Why I'm Kind Of Awesome Today:

MY AWESOMENESS GRADE FOR TODAY:

☐ A-   ☐ A   ☐ A+   ☐ A++

Besides,
They'll see how
beautiful I am
And be ashamed—
I, too, am
America.

Langston Hughes

─── Why I'm Kind Of Awesome Today: ───

MY AWESOMENESS GRADE FOR TODAY:

☐ A-　　　☐ A　　　☐ A+　　　☐ A++

We begin to find and become ourselves when we notice how we are already found, already truly, entirely, wildly, messily, marvelously who we were born to be.

Anne Lamott

Why I'm Kind Of Awesome Today:

MY AWESOMENESS GRADE FOR TODAY:

☐ A-   ☐ A   ☐ A+   ☐ A++

I celebrate myself, and sing myself,

And what I assume you shall assume,

For every atom belonging to me as good belongs to you.

Walt Whitman

Why I'm Kind Of Awesome Today:

MY AWESOMENESS GRADE FOR TODAY:

□ **A-**   □ **A**   □ **A+**   □ **A++**

I am a leaf on the wind, watch how I soar.

Keith R. A. DeCandido

Why I'm Kind Of Awesome Today:

MY AWESOMENESS GRADE FOR TODAY:

☐ A-   ☐ A   ☐ A+   ☐ A++

It is a blessing

to be the color
of earth

do you know
how often

flowers confuse
me for home

Why I'm Kind Of Awesome Today:

....

....

....

....

....

....

....

....

....

....

....

....

MY AWESOMENESS GRADE FOR TODAY:

☐ A-   ☐ A   ☐ A+   ☐ A++

Nothing is accomplished without making fools of ourselves.

Gloria Steinem

Why I'm Kind Of Awesome Today:

....

....

....

....

....

....

....

....

....

....

....

....

....

MY AWESOMENESS GRADE FOR TODAY:

☐ A-   ☐ A   ☐ A+   ☐ A++

This is the fast lane, folks...and some of us like it here.

Hunter S. Thompson

— Why I'm Kind Of Awesome Today: —

MY AWESOMENESS GRADE FOR TODAY:

☐ A-   ☐ A   ☐ A+   ☐ A++

Yup, you rule.

Knock Knock